POKéMON

SINNOH SUPERSTARS

ISBN-13: 978-0-545-10266-7
ISBN-10: 0-545-10266-9

Published by Scholastic Inc.
SCHOLASTIC and associated logos are trademarks and/or registered trademarks of Scholastic Inc.

12 11 10 9 8 7 6 5 4 3 2 1   8 9 10 11 12/0

Book designed by Henry Ng and Kay Petronio
Printed in the U.S.A.
First printing, September 2008

INSTRUCTIONS

How to use this book with a regular pencil.

Ready to draw all your favorite Pokémon?
Grab a pencil and get ready to go!

Step One

Choose your first Pokémon. Then tear out a sheet of tracing paper from the middle of the book. Place the sheet over the character you want to draw, leaving room for another Pokémon. Hold the paper still and trace.

Step Two

Pick out the next character you'd like to draw. Then position your tracing sheet over the Pokémon. You can even try moving the sheet around. A small change could make a big difference. Are the Pokémon friends? Are they battling? It's up to you! Once you've decided, hold the paper still and trace.

Step Three

Now that you're done tracing, you can add some color. You could try colored pencils, markers, paints, or whatever you have around.

How to use this book with 3-D glasses and drawing tool.

Did your book come with 3-D glasses and a special drawing tool? In that case, you can also use this book in a whole different way!

Are the pencils in your kit nice and sharp?

Good! Insert them into the tool with the points facing down, so they almost meet. They should line up like this:

Special Bonus

Then trace each image, keeping the blue line to the left of the red. Once you're done, put on your 3-D glasses to admire your work! Your image will look something like this:

Want to try something more? You can try varying the distance between the pencils for different effects. Or you could practice drawing with the 3-D glasses on to watch your super 3-D sketches take shape!

DRIFLOON

CROAGUNK

STUNKY

GLAMEOW

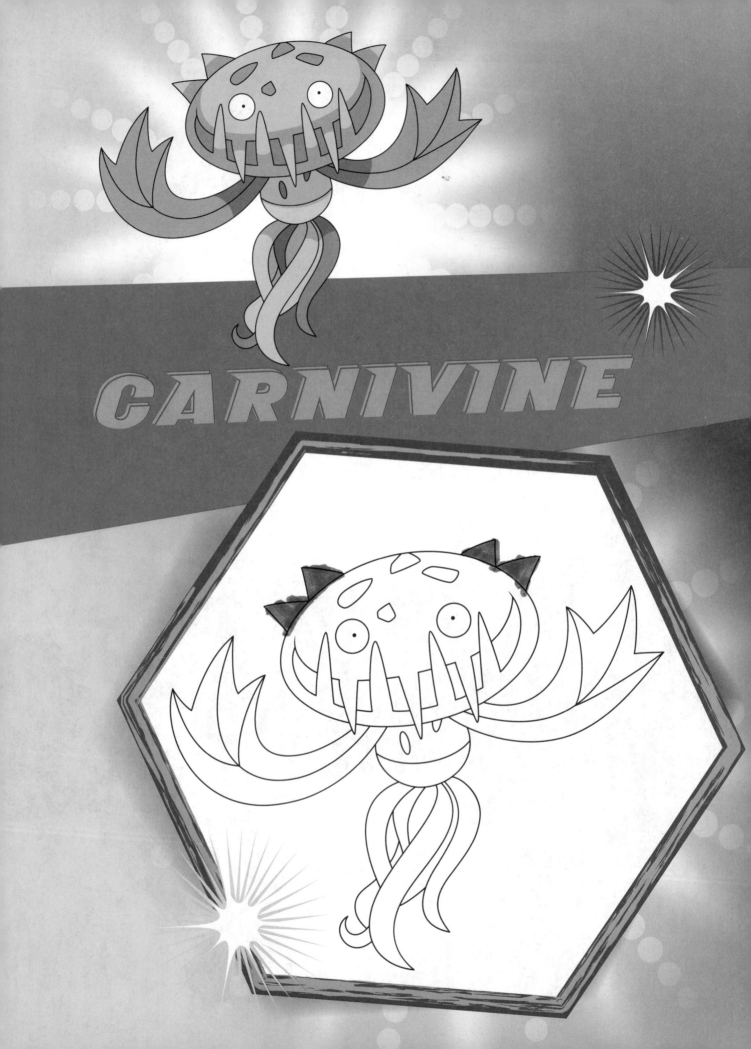

CARNIVINE

SKORUPI

SHINX

COMBEE

MISMAGIUS

HONCHKROW

DIALGA

PALKIA

DARKRAI